尾田栄一郎

People who put ♪ at the end of their sentences seem to be having more fun than necessary.

"We've started serving chilled noodles for the summer. ♪"

"I'm going to commit seppuku. ♪"

"I don't...want to...die. ♪"

When times are tough, add a musical note and blow away the blues. ♪

Volume 79...*is about to begin!* ♪ ♪

-Eiichiro Oda, 2015

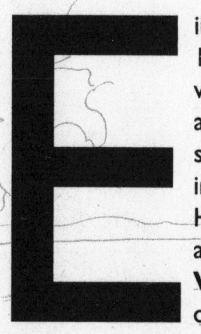

iichiro Oda began his manga career at the age of 17, when his one-shot cowboy manga **Wanted!** won second place in the coveted Tezuka manga awards. Oda went on to work as an assistant to some of the biggest manga artists in the industry, including Nobuhiro Watsuki, before winning the Hop Step Award for new artists. His pirate adventure **One Piece**, which debuted in **Weekly Shonen Jump** in 1997, quickly became one of the most popular manga in Japan.

ONE PIECE VOL. 79
NEW WORLD PART 19

SHONEN JUMP Manga Edition

STORY AND ART BY EIICHIRO ODA

Translation/Stephen Paul
Touch-up Art & Lettering/Vanessa Satone
Design/Fawn Lau
Editor/Alexis Kirsch

Printed in the U.S.A.

Published by VIZ Media, LLC
P.O. Box 77010
San Francisco, CA 94107

10 9 8 7 6 5 4 3 2 1
First printing, August 2016

www.viz.com

THE WORLD'S
MOST POPULAR MANGA
www.shonenjump.com

ONE PIECE

Vol. 79
LUCY!!

STORY AND ART BY
EIICHIRO ODA

The Straw Hat Crew

Tony Tony Chopper

After researching powerful medicine in Birdie Kingdom, he reunited with the rest of the crew.

Ship's Doctor, Bounty: 50 berries

Monkey D. Luffy

A young man who dreams of becoming the Pirate King. After training with Rayleigh, he and his crew head for the New World!

Captain, Bounty: 400 million berries

Nico Robin

She spent her time in Baltigo with the leader of the Revolutionary Army: Luffy's father, Dragon.

Archeologist, Bounty: 80 million berries

Roronoa Zolo

He swallowed his pride and asked to be trained by Mihawk on Gloom Island before reuniting with the rest of the crew.

Fighter, Bounty: 120 million berries

Franky

He modified himself in Future Land Baldimore and turned himself into Armored Franky before reuniting with the rest of the crew.

Shipwright, Bounty: 44 million berries

Nami

She studied the weather of the New World on the small Sky Island Weatheria, a place where weather is studied as a science.

Navigator, Bounty: 16 million berries

Brook

After being captured and used as a freak show by the Longarm Tribe, he became a famous rock star called "Soul King" Brook.

Musician, Bounty: 33 million berries

Usopp

He trained under Heracles at the Bowin Islands to become the King of Snipers.

Sniper, Bounty: 30 million berries

Shanks

One of the Four Emperors. Waits for Luffy in the "New World," the second half of the Grand Line.

Captain of the Red-Haired Pirates

Sanji

After fighting the New Kama Karate masters in the Kamabakka Kingdom, he returned to the crew.

Cook, Bounty: 77 million berries

one-legged toy soldier who informs them of the nation's hidden darkness, and they decide to help the little Tontattas in their fight for freedom. While their companions defeat the DQ Family officers, the "birdcage" surrounding the island begins to shrink, threatening to slice everyone to bits... Luffy and Law team up to fight Doflamingo directly, but Law gets knocked out of the battle. It's all up to Luffy now. He unleashes the tremendous Gear Four to counteract Doflamingo's strength, but will that be enough...?

The story of ONE PIECE 1»79

Don Quixote Pirates

Don Quixote Doflamingo (Joker)

One of the Seven Warlords of the sea and a weapons broker. He works under the alias of "Joker."

Pirate, Warlord

Supreme Officer: Vergo

Officer: Monet

Bellamy the Hyena
Ex-captain of Bellamy Pirates

Pica Army ♠

Assault Squad

Gladius

Buffalo

Baby 5

Diamante Army ♦

Fighter Brigade

Lao G | Señor Pink

Machvise | Dellinger

Trebol Army ♣

Special Powers Team

Sugar

Violet

Giolla

→ Viola
Former Princess, Rebecca's Aunt

Riku Doldo III
Former King of Dressrosa

Rebecca
Gladiator (Riku's G.Daughter)

Kyros (former toy)
Rebecca's Father

Sabo

Brother in spirit to Ace and Luffy. He was shot by Celestial Dragons and assumed dead.

Revolutionary Army Chief of Staff

Corazon

Doflamingo's younger brother. Tried to heal Law's sickness, but was murdered by his own brother.

Former Heart Commander of DQ Family

Fujitora (Issho)

A blind swordsman. One of the Three Admirals after Aokiji's departure.

Naval HQ Admiral

Trafalgar Law

The Surgeon of Death, wielder of the Op-Op Fruit's powers. Currently allied with Luffy.

Pirate, Warlord (Tentative)

Story

After two years of hard training, the Straw Hat pirates are back together, first at the Sabaody Archipelago and then through Fish-Man Island to their next stage: the New World!!

The crew happens across Trafalgar Law on the island of Punk Hazard. At his suggestion, they form a new pirate alliance that seeks to take down one of the Four Emperors. The group infiltrates the kingdom of Dressrosa in an attempt to set up Doflamingo, but Law is abducted after falling into a trap. The rest of the crew meets a

NEW WORLD

Vol. 79
LUCY!!

CONTENTS

Chapter 786:
GYATS

REQUEST: "LUFFY AND A MONKEY TRYING TO GET LAW TO EAT BREAD" BY GREEDY OFG

WAY TO GO, RUBBER BALL!!!

AAAA!

HE DID IT!!

HUFF !!

HUFF !!

...STRAW HAT LUFFY!!!

RAAAAAAH!

YOU'RE THE PIRATE...

NO, I REMEMBER WHAT KING RIKU CALLED YOU...

WHY DOES HE KEEP BOUNCING AROUND THOUGH?! CAN'T HE STOP?!

AW, SHUDDUP.

BUT I HEARD HE WAS A 25-FOOT-TALL MONSTER!! HE CAN'T BE MORE THAN A DOZEN!

HUFF, HUFF... WEEZ!

BUT HE LOOKS SCARIER AND ROUNDER THAN THE FACE IN THE PAPER! IS THAT REALLY HIM?!

NOPE.

BOING!

WEEZ WEEZ...

BOING!

YEAH.

HUH?

HE... WON?!!

REALLY?!!

IT WAS STRAW HAT!!

VIOLA!!

HEY, WHAT WAS THAT CRAZY NOISE?!

RAAAAH

WHAT DESTRUCTIVE POWER!! THERE'S NO WAY HE CAN STILL BE ALIVE!!

GR...

R...RGG...

YOU BEAT DOFLA-MINGO!!!

RAAAAHH

BOING

BUT HEY, YOU DID IT!!

HUFF...

BOING

LOOK UP ABOVE US...

HUFF, HUFF...

NOT ENOUGH.

HUH?

THE BIRD-CAGE HASN'T DISAPPEARED YET!!!

BASH

OOM!!

!!!

HEY, WHAT HAPPENED?!

GWON-k!!

BLOp!

BLOp!!

HUH?!

WEEZ!

GURK...

GURK...

STRAW HAT LUFFY?!

FSH

WEEZ!

...!!!

AAAH!! **WHUMP!!** EYAAAH!!!

SNOOOOUS...H!!

WEE HAW HAW HAW!

IT'S BURGESS THE CHAMPION!!!

WHAT THE--?!!

RAAHH

GYAA

STILL, WE CAN'T TRUST HIM!! HE'S A PIRATE!!

BUT KING RIKU SAID HE WAS OUR ONLY HOPE!!!

WE DON'T KNOW WHAT HE'S PLOTTING!!

NO, STAY BACK!!

RAAHA

MURMUR

WOBBLE

WOBBLE

MURMUR

...?!

HE'S A PIRATE TOO!!

CRAK!! CRAK!! CRAK! CRAK! CRAK

...

WHAT HAPPENED TO DOFLAMINGO...?

?!!

HUFF!!

HUFF!!

HEY, TELL US! IS THE FIGHT OVER?!

(Igarashi, Oita)

Q: Hey…Odacchi!! *Koff*… This ain't got nothin' to do with you, but…*huff*… In that alley back there to the right…I saw a weak ol' grandma who needed help! *Tek-tek-tek* (Odacchi runs off!) …All right! \(^o^)/ Finally!

Start the SBS! ★
Yay! I said it!

--Ayataro

BUT IN THE ALLEY TO THE RIGHT BACK THERE…

A: …? Hmm, that's weird. I looked all over and didn't find any Grandmas… **Hey!! The SBS started without me!!** Damn, I Got tricked! Still, I'm Glad!! At least there were no…poor ol' Grandmas in trouble…

Q: In Japanese, "ni-ko" means "two objects." Is Nico Robin called Nico because she has two big boobs?

--Hiromu

A: No.

Q: It's nice to meet you. If you don't mind, could you tell me the secret to drawing the hourglass figures of the women in *One Piece?!* (Especially the boobs) Thank you! ♡ --If There Is No Bread, Let Them Eat Roses

A: Yes. Hello. This is the special SBS drawing lesson. Just think of the female figure as three circles and one X. And now, Goodbye. (If this is the only figure you draw, your female readers will send you many criticisms. Try to remain strong and dedicated.)

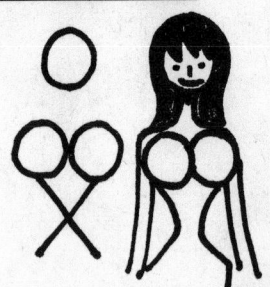

Chapter 787:
FOUR MINUTES BEFORE

REQUEST: "ZORO AND BEARS WEARING HAPPI COATS AND HEADBANDS, BEATING TAIKO DRUMS" BY MASAO FROM GIFU

AND NO ONE ELSE CAN HAVE IT! IT'S OUR MEMENTO OF HIM.

HUH!

HUFF!! SABO! SO YOU GOT... ACE'S FRUIT, HUH?

KEEP HIM SAFE, PETS!!

DADUM!!

IT'S GYATS!! AND I WILL!!

...IS MINE!!!

THAT POWER...

RA AH

KADOO

LARIAT!!!

GALLEON...

AAAGH!!

FWUM!!

DO OM!!

?!!!!

HURF!!

HURF!!

GET OUT HERE, STRAW HAT!! YOU WILL RUE THIS MISTAKE !!!

YOU MISERABLE RATS!! I DON'T NEED ANY STAMINA...

...TO ELIMINATE THE LIKES OF YOU!!

UNBELIEVABLE... HOW DOES HE STILL HAVE SO MUCH STAMINA?!

WHOA ...

DON'T FALTER NOW! WE'VE GOT TO SLOW HIM DOWN!!

(Hippo Iron, Saitama)

Q: On page 39 of volume 74, there's a scene where Doflamingo's followers go quiet in the elevator. When I was a boy, my parents taught me to be silent in the elevator. Are they following the same lesson?

--Hiromu

A: Mmm, yes, they got quiet. What's up with that humorous pause, huh? If someone farted, that would pretty much be the perfect accident.

Q: The best cook on the Straw Hat Crew is obviously Sanji, but who else is good at cooking? What is everyone's specialty?

--I Made the Mantis Chicken

A: Here's the dish each member is good at making.

 Raw meat on a plate  Sashimi Roast duck in tangerine sauce  Fish and chips

 Mixed juice  Stew, paella Barbecue Churrasco

Sanji is most experienced with seafood, but he can cook pretty much anything. Due to their upbringing, the only decent cooks are Nami, Usopp and Robin. The others can't do much more than cut, burn, and mix. Even to her own crewmates, Nami charges for her food.

Chapter 788:
MY BATTLE

REQUEST: "PERONA GROOVING OUT TO BROOK'S CURSED SONG PERFORMANCE" BY MARRON PARFAIT FROM TOYAMA

THREE MINUTES UNTIL THE BIRDCAGE REACHES THE TOWN CENTER...

AAAAAAAHHH!!

IT'S SHRINKING FASTER NOW!!

RUN FOR YOUR LIVES!!

HE'S GOING TO SLICE UP THE ENTIRE COUNTRY BEFORE LUCY CAN RECOVER!!

HE'S REALLY DONE IT NOW!!

TAKE DOWN DOFLAMINGO AND ELIMINATE THE BIRD-CAGE!!!

WE'VE JUST GOTTA HANDLE THIS OUR-SELVES!!!

I GAVE YOU A MESSAGE: BRING ME STRAW HAT.

YOU PEOPLE JUST DON'T GET IT...

RAAH!!

WE'RE NOT GOING TO HAND HIM OVER...

I KNOW THAT!!

BUT WE'LL HAVE MASS FATALITIES BEFORE THAT POINT!!

THERE'S STILL THREE AND A HALF MINUTES UNTIL LUCY RECOVERS!!

BOOM.

HANG ON, GYATS!!

...UNTIL HE'S READY!!!

BUT YOU DON'T THROW A FIGHTER INTO THE RING WHEN YOU KNOW HE CAN'T FIGHT!!

RAAAH!

WHOA!!

FUMP!!

POP!!

HMM?

DON'T YOU THINK YOU'RE RUNNING A BIT *TOO* FAR AWAY...?

HUFF!!

HUFF!!

TUH--!! TUH-TUH-TUH!! TRAFALGAR LAW!!!

WUH-WULLA-WARLORD OF THE SEA!!!

DRIP!!

DRIP!!

IS HIS HAKI RETURNING TO HIM?!

...I'LL TAKE HIM FROM HERE.

YES, SIR!!

EVERY MOMENT COUNTS, THEN...

HE TOLD US HE NEEDED TEN MINUTES, SO HE'S GOT, UH... THREE MINUTES, TWENTY SECONDS TO GO!!

...FWOM PWINCESS MANSHERRY'S HEALING TEARS!

DEY'RE DANDELIONS MADE...

DAT'S WIGHT!!

DANDELIXIRS?

YA-R-R-GH!

BUT I JUST CAN'T!! WHY'D I HAVE TO SPRAIN MY ANKLE NOW, OF ALL TIMES?!

HURRY UP!! JUST RUN FASTER!!

CRAK CRUNCH!!

RAAAAÄAHH

EEEK!!

HELP ME!! I'M GONNA GET SLICED TO BITS!!

FHUF

RAH...

FHUF

KYAA...HH

FHUF

WAIT, HOW ARE YOU THAT FAST?! THAT MAKES NO SENSE!!

BAZOOM!!

WHAT THE--?!! I CAN RUN!!

HASH!

HANG IN DERE.

RAH...

RAH...!

KPAA...!

WHAT?!

FATHER, IF IT SHOULD COME TO IT, I'M READY TO...

I WON'T LET YOU DO THAT, DOFLAMINGO!!

DASH!!

...THEN ALL OF THIS IS FOR NAUGHT!! EVERYONE'S SUFFERING IS WASTED!!

VIOLA?!!

DO

OM!!

THEN WHY ARE *YOU* HERE, VIOLA?

IF I LET YOU DIE, HOW COULD I EVER SHOW MY FACE...

...TO BROTHER KYROS OR MY LATE SISTER AGAIN?

RAH!!

RAH!!

REBECCA!! WHAT ARE YOU DOING HERE?!

DON'T GET ANY STUPID IDEAS!

YOU CAN'T--!!

...WOULDN'T IT BE A TAD TOO CONVENIENT FOR ME TO JUST WALK AWAY...

...HAVING ONCE BEEN AN OFFICER MYSELF?!

FL

AP..!!

IF THE DON QUIXOTE FAMILY IS GOING TO COLLAPSE INTO NOTHING...

HEE HEE... WHAT A PASSIONATE DECISION, VIOLET.

"DOFY" !!

RAHH!

RAHH!

EITHER I DIE... OR YOU DIE!!

IT'S TOO DANGEROUS UP AHEAD FOR US TO KEEP GOING!!

CHATTER CHATTER.

PRETTY MUCH THE ENTIRE COUNTRY IS PACKED UP HERE!!

BAM!

CHATTER CHATTER

LET US IN! WE RAN ALL THE WAY HERE!!

THE BIRDCAGE IS NEARLY UPON THIS SPOT!!

TOWN CENTER

CHATTER CHATTER

HEY!!

HMM ?

RRRMM..!

...!!

IT'S MOVING AGAIN!!!

CLINK..

CLUNK..

OH...

HUFF !!

HUFF !!

HEH HEH...

ZZRRD

SBS Question Corner

(Patrick, Osaka)

A: It's time for a game! This one comes from "Yucchan's Papa"! Thank you very much! Find the seven differences! Cover up the answers below so you don't see them.

(1) Door frame (2) Door handle (3) Nami's belt (4) Sanji's cigarette (5) Sanji's pants hem (6) Law's sword pattern (7) Chopper's mouth

Chapter 789:
LUCY!!

REQUEST: "SHANKS AND A BULLDOG CHILLING UNDER A CAFÉ TERRACE" BY YASSU FROM CHIBA

ZZRO

?!!

We stopped it for a moment earlier...

Hang in there! Keep pushing!!

ZZRO

ZZRO

GAK GAK..!!
RAAAAAAAAAAHH...!!

...but now the center's about to burst!!

ZZRO.

Hurry, tank!!

GRAK GRAK!!

It's finally starting to cut into the royal plateau!!!

RAAAAH!
RAH
RAH

GRUDD

Yes, majesty!!

Commander tank!!

King Riku!!!

Huh ?!

DO

D3!!

WHAM WHAM!!

AH !!
BING!!
BUT ...
...I WILL NEVER FORGIVE BETRAYAL !!
?!!
DOOM!!
ZSH ZSH..
UH...!!
VIOLA ...
I CAN'T CONTROL... MY BODY!!
STOP THIS!!
LEAVE REBECCA OUT OF IT!!
KILL HER!!
!!
ZSH
ZSH
NO...NO! WHAT AM I DOING?!
...!!!
REBECCA !!
VIOLA...
...I DON'T WANT TO DO THIS!!!
GRAAAAAAHH..
GRRMMMM..

OUR STAR, LUCY...
ROT IN HELL, DOFLAMINGO...
RAAHH
...WILL SINK YOU IN ONE HIT!!!
RAAHH
ZSH ZSH
DODGE OUT OF THE WAY!
PLEASE, VIOLA!!
CLOSE YOUR EYES, REBECCA!!
YOU DON'T HAVE TO SEE ANY OF IT!! THIS IS A NIGHTMARE!! NO MATTER WHAT HAPPENS, JUST FORGET IT ALL!!
DRIP
DRIP
AAH !!
I WON'T BLAME YOU FOR ANY-THING!!
JUST FORGET IT!! YOU'VE DONE NOTHING WRONG!!!
NOOOOO !!!
I'M SO SORRY, REBECCA...
FOR LEAVING THESE TERRIBLE SCARS ON YOUR HEART!!
RAAAAH

HEAVEN AND EARTH

Chapter 790

ONE PIECE vol.79

KABOOM!!

?!!

POP!

POP!

EEK!

THUMP!!

OOF!!

REBECCA!!

WEEZ...

VUB VUB VUB VUB VUR...

HMPH!

JUST WATCH THIS...

THERE YOU ARE...

WHAM!! WHAM! HRRGH!!!

KCHI NG!!

ARMA-MENT!!

DMMDMMDMA ...!! SHWDD!! AAAH!!!

BLORP!

HAS YOUR HAKI *REALLY* COME BACK, "LUCY"?!

UNG...

DRIP DRIP

KABOO--M!!!

!!!

!!

DADADADAMM!!

?!!

AAAAHH!!

LUCY!!!

D r r m...

HURRY UP, LUCY!!!

NO, THE BIRDCAGE AIN'T GONE YET...

RAAH!!

DID LUCY WIN?!

MUTTER

MUTTER

AND THAT HUGE DUST CLOUD!!

WHAT A SOUND!!

RAAAAAAAHH

FLOWER

MUR-MUR

MUR-MUR

YOU PULLED THROUGH BY THE SKIN OF YOUR TEETH AGAIN, LUFFY.

RAAAAAHH

KSHUNK...!!

UGH... MY BODY'S MOVING... ON ITS OWN!!

HRP!!

CLUNK!!

...!!

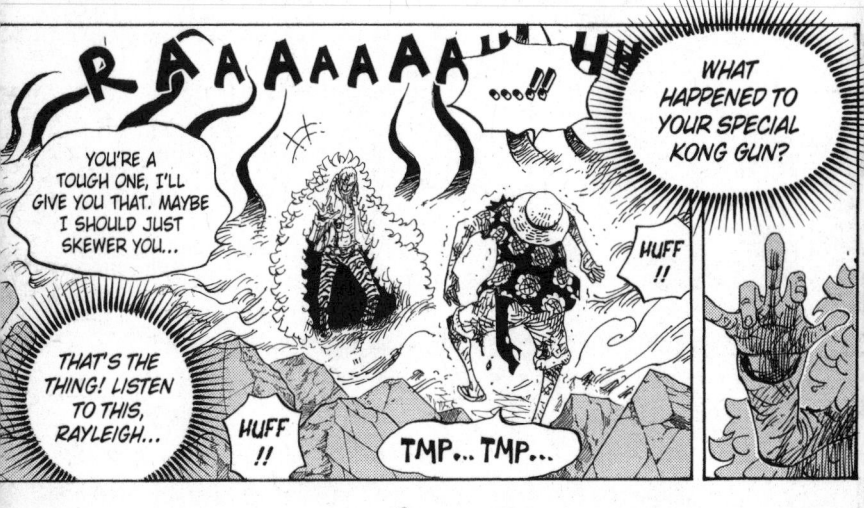

RAAAAAAAAAHH

YOU'RE A TOUGH ONE, I'LL GIVE YOU THAT. MAYBE I SHOULD JUST SKEWER YOU...

THAT'S THE THING! LISTEN TO THIS, RAYLEIGH...

HUFF !!

...!!

WHAT HAPPENED TO YOUR SPECIAL KONG GUN?

HUFF !!

HUFF !!

TMP... TMP...

IN THAT CASE, YOU BETTER THINK OF A DIFFERENT METHOD. THE PROBLEM WITH GEAR FOUR...

...IS THAT IT PLACES TOO MUCH STRAIN ON YOUR BODY.

RAHH

HA HA HA! SOUNDS LIKE TROUBLE.

THERE WAS AN EVEN BIGGER ONE THIS TIME, AND THE MOVE DIDN'T WORK!!

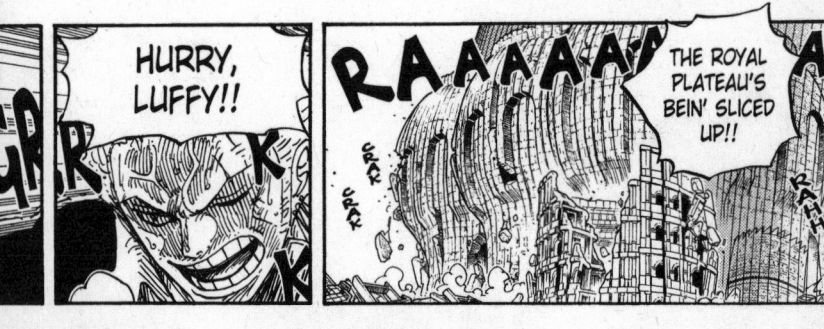

ENOUGH OF THIS!!!

...I WOULDN'T HAVE HAD TO SLAUGHTER THEM ALL!!

IF ONLY THEY'D ALL BEHAVED THEMSELVES AND DANCED ON MY STRINGS INSIDE THE CAGE...

HUFF, HUFF...

ZSH ZSH ZSH

HUFF, HUFF...

DANCE ...?

CAGE ...?

HURRY, LUFFY!!

GRR K

RAAAAA-

URKK URKK

THE ROYAL PLATEAU'S BEIN' SLICED UP!!

AH

DOO-M

SNAP!!! SNAP!!

GEAR FOUR !!!!

SNAP SNAP!!

•••

THERE YOU GO...

IN ONE AREA...

CRAASH!!

...ARE KNOWN AS...

...THE PEOPLE OF THE D...

UMM.

...THE ENEMIES OF THE GODS.

CLAKK--!!

SBS Question Corner

(Masamichi Kobayashi, Gunma)

Q: Odacchi!! Here's an idea: what would the three Don Quixote supreme officers, Trebol, Diamante and Pica, look like if they got hit by Sanji's Parage Shot?!
--Softball Fool ⑭

A: Here.

Q: Is it just me, or do the Devil Fruit Powers of the officers on Doflamingo's side all have powered-up versions of the Baroque Works officers?
Ton-Ton -> Kilo-Kilo, Stick-Stick -> Wax-Wax, Arms-Arms -> Dice-Dice, Pop-Pop -> Boom-Boom

--Taoka S43

A: There are indeed higher-powered versions of others, but at present it's only these four.

 Ton-Ton >  Kilo-Kilo   Chilly-Chilly > Snow-Snow

 Mag-Mag > Flame-Flame    Arms-Arms > Dice-Dice

There are some other fruit which might seem to be related, but in those cases, the rules that determine their powers work in slightly different ways. Also, the strength of powers does not correlate to character strength. You never know how every fight will turn out.

100

Chapter 791: *RUBBLE*

REQUEST: "PLEASE DRAW CHOPPER, SANJI AND TWO MICE BAKING BREAD" BY SHINORITA FROM ITABASHI

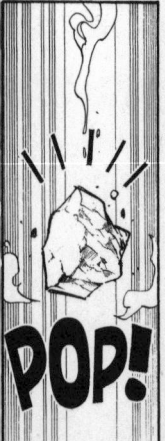

GRRG

LUCY
!!

THUDD··!!

GRRG.

KRSH

CRUMBLE

DOCK, UNDERGROUND TRADING PORT

CLAKK!!

CLUNK...

TELL US, GYATS!!!

WHAT JUST HAPPENED?!

•••

WHAT'S GOING ON?!

THERE'S NO ONE IN THE SKY!!

RAHH GYAA RAHH

LOOK...UP THERE!

?!

HUFF, HUFF... DON'T BE STUPID...

WHAT KIND OF COMMENTATOR... FAILS TO CROWN THE WINNER...?

DON'T HURT YOUR-SELF!!

RAHH

CLICK..!

WOBBLE...

GYATS, YOU CAN'T KEEP SHOUTING IN THIS CONDITION!

RAHH

MARK MY WORD!

I WON'T LET THE TOY SOLDIER DIE!! SO STAY SAFE!!

REBECCA! DON'T CRY YET!!

SPLISH...

SPLISH...

SPLISH...

GRMM RAAHH HNNG...

DO!!

THE WINNER IS--!!!

THE WIM...

OM!!

...GONNA CRUSH DOFLAMINGO!!!

I'M TOTALLY...

DRIP.

DRIP.

LUCY...

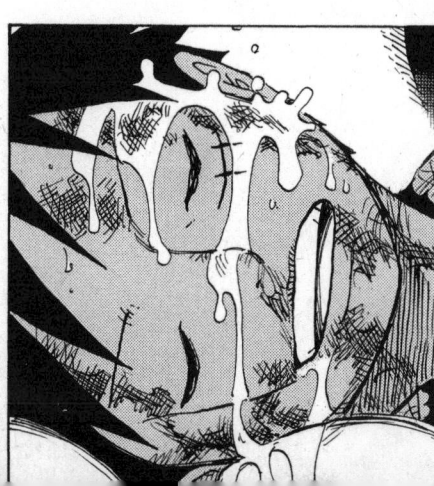

...!!!

HUFFF!

RATTLE.

RATTLE.

DRIP. DRIP.

AND SO DA CAPTAIN HAS FOUGHT FOR TEN LONG YEARS!!

EVEN IF THESE TIN EYES CAN NO LONGER SHED TEARS OF THEIR OWN...

EVEN A TOY MUST PROTECT THAT WHICH IS DEAR TO IT.

...

RA...AH

THIS BATTLE BEGAN TEN YEARS AGO!!

RA...AH

RAAAH

...

H

WE FIGHT...

THUMP

RAAAH.

RAAAAH

ZSH...

ZSH...

WE FIGHT TO RESTORE THE HONOR...

...OF THE DEPOSED KING RIKU...

質問コーナー

(Fujima, Fukuoka)

Q: Odacchi!! Hello, ha-ha. About Dr. Hiriluk's birthday, the word "doctor" in Japanese can be turned into the numbers 1, 4 and 8, so how about January 12th?

--Ha-P Haruka

A: Hiriluk? Now?! If you think you can just decide it that easily...you're right!! 👍
So that's settled.
(H)ey (E)veryone (L)isten (F)or a (S)econd!

It's HELFS time!!

You know how everyone comes up with the Birthdays on their own? That's totally fine, since to Be honest, I don't care aBout the characters' Birthdays. (There, I said it.) Anyway, I sat down with my editor and looked up all the Birthdays we've got so far. The "Birthday calendar" is in the Back of this Book. Check it out! You'll find that...lots of them overlap!! Meanwhile, I've Gotten plenty of letters saying, "I don't share my Birthday with any characters."

So what that means is, let's fill the calendar!!

Let's make it so that everyone can say they share a Birthday with someone in One Piece. And let me Be clear.
I'm not GoinG to douBle-check!! You all have to fill in the Blanks using whatever twisted logic you can come up with. I will proBaBly approve everything, just as I have so far.

Because I really don't care!!

The calendar is current as of OctoBer 2015, so it will Get more crowded with each successive volume. You can write in the characters yourself, and we'll Be puttinG a Birthday calendar up on One-Piece.com that will Be updated reGularly, so if you want to come up with a character's Birthday, check out which dates are empty there Before you send them in. Thanks!

Chapter 792:
ON HANDS AND KNEES

REQUEST: "LEO GETTING FIREFLIES TO WRITE
HAPPY BIRTHDAY IN THE NIGHT SKY FOR MANSHERRY"
BY HIRO MORITAKA FROM HYOGO

WAAHH

RÁAAAAAAHH

...!!

3

HUFF!

AHH

YOU AREN'T
GOING...TO
FINISH ME?!

NO
NEED.

RAAH

RAA

...

RR!
RRR

?!

YOU'RE ALL
TOO SOFT...YOU
BROTHERS!!

WEE...
HA...HA!!

I THINK IT'S
ALL OVER
NOW...

RAAH

CLINK..

RR!
RRR

"DON'T TELL MY BROTHER."

OF *COURSE* THEY WERE GOING TO REPORT TO THE ENTIRE WORLD THAT THE INFAMOUS FIRE FIST ACE WAS BROUGHT TO JUSTICE!!

HE HAD NO IDEA OF THE VALUE OF HIS LIFE.

WHAT A FOOL!

ENOUGH... STOP TALKING!!

I'VE SPENT TIME THINKING ABOUT HIS LAST THOUGHTS ON EARTH...

THE MILITARY MADE SURE TO GET 120 PERCENT OF WHAT HIS LIFE WAS WORTH--

EVEN WITH THE MISUNDERSTANDING FIXED...I CANNOT RETURN TO THE THRONE.

PLEASE, NO... NONE OF THAT.

KING RIKU!! SCORES OF OUR COUNTRYMEN WERE TURNED INTO MUTE TOYS!!

NO... WHEN PUSH COMES TO SHOVE, THE RIKU FAMILY IDEALS ARE BRITTLE AND WEAK.

WHAT IF EVERYONE IN THE KINGDOM SHARED YOUR WAY OF THINKING?! WOULD YOU DO IT THEN?!

WE'VE HAD ENOUGH OF VIOLENCE!!

NO! YOU'RE THE ONLY KING FOR THIS COUNTRY!!

THAT HAS BEEN PROVEN BY THIS WHOLE DEBACLE...

...!!!

IF IT CAUSES OUR LAND TO COLLAPSE...WELL, WE'RE WILLING TO RISK THAT!!!

WE WANT YOU TO BE THE *KING WHO WON'T FIGHT!* WE WANT YOU TO RESIST WAR!!

?!

WE DON'T CARE IF WE FALL INTO RUIN!!!

ZSH..!!

YOU ARE RIKU DOLDO, KING OF MIRACLES!!!

COME BACK TO US.

ooo

ooooo!!

...TAKE ALL THE BLAME FOR THE HELL DOFLAMINGO RAISED.

WE CAN'T GO HAVIN' YOU...

?!

GOOD KING RIKU!!

INDEED, INDEED...

FUJITORA!!

MURMUR MURMUR!

ZSH ZSH

PEOPLE OF THE KINGDOM...

...IS NONE OTHER THAN THE **WORLD GOVERN-MENT!!**

...UNDER THE AUTHORITY OF THE **WARLORDS OF THE SEA** SYSTEM...

THE FORCE RESPONSIBLE FOR LETTIN' THAT VICIOUS PIRATE HOLD OFFICIAL REIGN...

PEOPLE OF THE ROYAL FAMILY...

Chapter 793:
TIGER AND DOG

REQUEST: "CHOPPER CAN'T TELL THE DIFFERENCE BETWEEN A TENGU, PINOCCHIO, AND USOPP" BY HAZUKI ITO FROM FUKUSHIMA

AN ADMIRAL FROM NAVY HQ...

AN...

GRRRG OHH...

RAISE YOUR HEAD, FUJITORA.

AND THERE'S A VISUAL TRANSPONDER SNAIL RECORDING IT ALL!

MURMUR!

MURMUR

BOWING DOWN TO US!!

MUR

HOW COULD A MAN WHO LET PIRATES RUN WILD ON INNOCENT FOLKS TURN HIS BLADE ON A WARLORD OF THE SEA...

GRRRG

正義

WHAT I NEEDED WAS THE TRUTH!! SO I CHOSE TO LET *THEM*...

DO YOU REALLY WANT THE WORLD TO SEE THIS SPECTACLE?!

...AND THEN ACT AS THOUGH HE DISPENSES JUSTICE?

THAT WAS MY GAMBLE.

...DO ALL THE FIGHTIN'.

IN FACT...DID YOU CHOOSE NOT TO GO AFTER DOFLAMINGO, JUST TO SET THIS MOMENT UP?!

ZW ZWIP!!

...THAT THIS COUNTRY SEIZED VICTORY TODAY!!

...OF PIRATES, GLADIATORS AND CITIZENS...

IT WAS THROUGH THE ACTIONS...

WELL DONE, EVERYONE...

RAAAAAAHH
RAH KAA RAH

ZWIP!!

THE LITTLE RIKU ARMY!!

YOU ARE THE ANTI-DOFLAMINGO FORCE...

YESSUH, CAP'N!!

HA HA! GO ON TO SEE KING RIKU IN THE PALACE NOW.

WE WILL!!

WAAH

CAPTAAAIN!!

CAPTAIN!!

WAAH

...IS DIS-BANDED!!

AND NOW ALL OF OUR GOALS HAVE BEEN MET! AS OF TODAY, THIS UNIT...

AND SEND EVERYONE WHO'S LOST THEIR HOME TO THE PALACE AS WELL, IF YOU DON'T MIND!

WITH PLEASURE, YOUR MAJESTY!

CHATTER CHATTER

TANK! THE NAVY HAS AN IMAGE TO UPHOLD.

...AND HIDE THEM IN THE PALACE.

TAKE THE PIRATES AND GLADIATORS WHO FOUGHT FOR OUR SAKE...

THE DEAL'S IN THE BOOKS!!

BUT WE'VE ALREADY PAID THE MONEY!!

YOU CAN'T DO THIS TO US, JOKER!!!

GRRg.

RAAA

THE WAR'S COMING TO AN END!!!

IF ONLY *THEY* HADN'T SHOWN UP!!!

GRAA

WHAT HAPPENS TO OUR *SMILE* TRANSACTION?!!

MY DEVIL FRUIT DEAL'S FALLEN THROUGH!!

THE WEAPONS MUST STILL BE IN DRESSROSA!!

DON'T EVEN THINK ABOUT IT! THAT ADMIRAL'S DOWN THERE!!

SHUNK SHUNK!!

*TSURU

THEN AGAIN, I SUPPOSE YOU *HAVE* BEEN ON THESE PIRATES' TRAIL FOR SOME TIME.

THAT'S WHAT *I'M* SAYING, INSPECTOR GENERAL!!

YOU DIDN'T NEED TO SET SAIL.

WHAT'S UP, TSURU DOLL?!

ON YOUR ORDERS!!

WANT A CRACKER?

GRR

DOOM!!

FSSHHH!

GG.

ZZSHH

CREAK...!

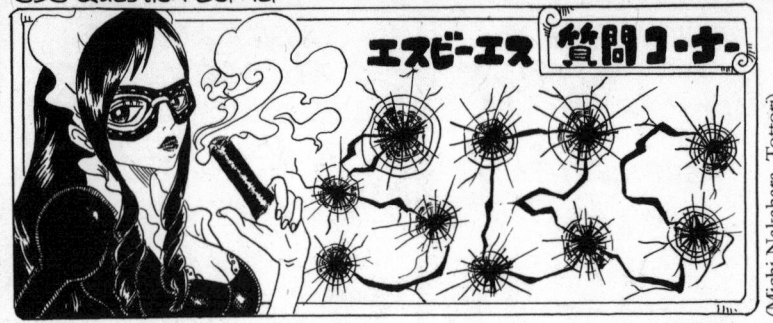

(Michi Nakahara, Tottori)

Q: Oda Sensei! Hello! I feel like Luffy's Gear Four pose is very similar to the Nio statues that stand outside Buddhist temples. Is there a deeper meaning to this very cool pose? I am thinking of using it the next time we have a marital spat.

--Sanadacchi

A: So this letter is from a husband. Personally, if you have a fight with your wife, I recommend Fujitora's "bowing on hands and knees" pose. (laughs) You are correct that I used the Nio statue pose! I came up with a number of different power-ups based on various cultures around the world, but I decided to go with something that displayed the strength of ancient Japan. I really want to see Gear Four in the anime and figures.

Q: Guess what I found, Oda Sensei. There are people in Chapter 785 wearing shirts with messages from the dialogue written on them. Does this mean that Doflamingo was importing the latest fashion straight from Fish-Man Island?

--The Self-Sacrificing Swordsman

A: Spotted again. It's the return of the "narrative description" shirts. Yes, the ultra-chic NDS brand has made its way from Fish-Man Island to Dressrosa. I'm sure there are more out there. Look for them yourself! My personal favorite is the "ATAMANOTOGATTAKO" (Kid With the Pointy Head) series.

It's King Riku

Isn't it?!

Got it!

Survive!!

Chapter 794: SABO'S ADVENTURE

REQUEST: "DOFLAMINGO LENDS A FLAMINGO HIS SHADES" BY FOREST RESIDENT FROM TOCHIGI

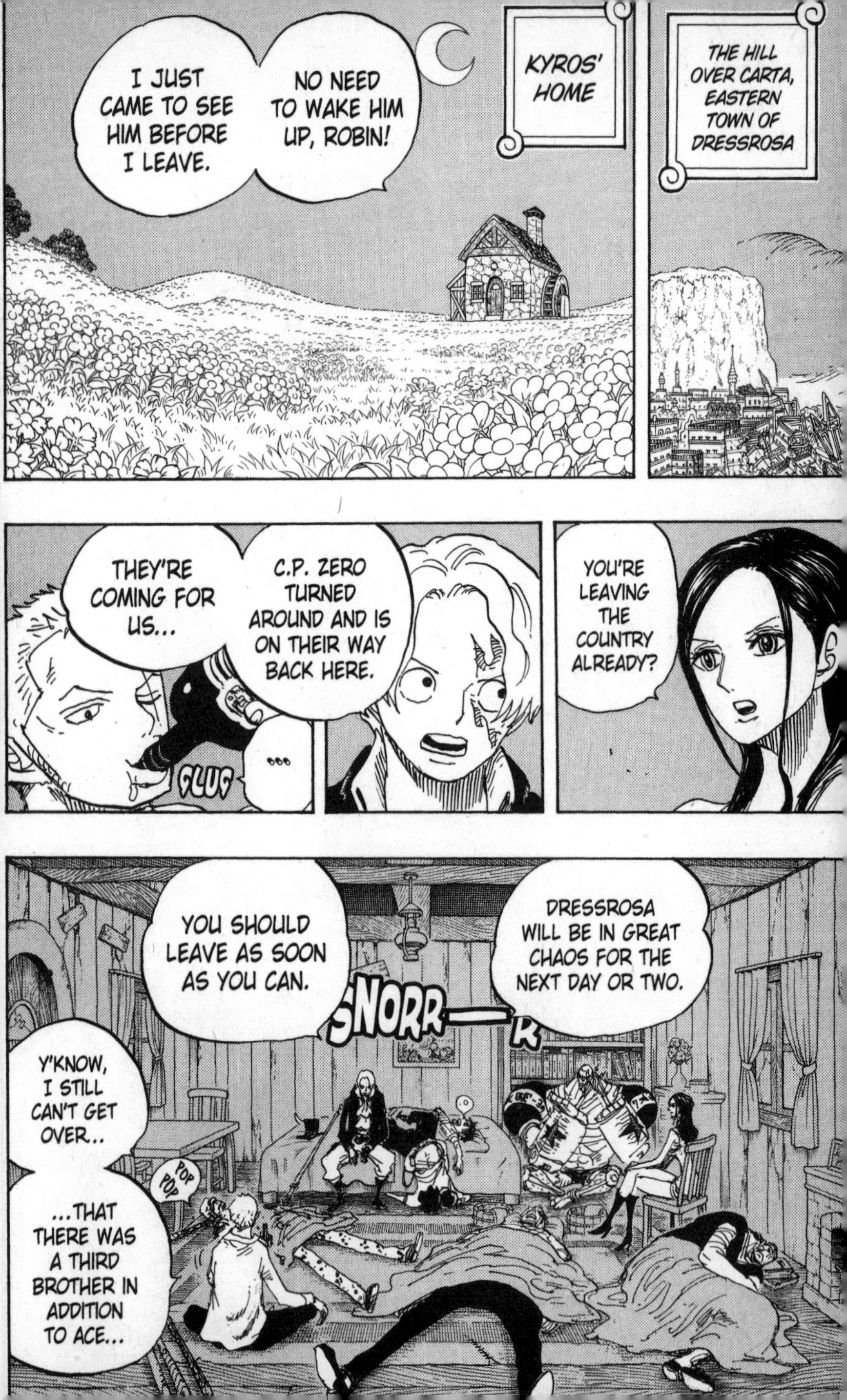

KYROS' HOME

THE HILL OVER CARTA, EASTERN TOWN OF DRESSROSA

I JUST CAME TO SEE HIM BEFORE I LEAVE.

NO NEED TO WAKE HIM UP, ROBIN!

THEY'RE COMING FOR US...

C.P. ZERO TURNED AROUND AND IS ON THEIR WAY BACK HERE.

GLUG

YOU'RE LEAVING THE COUNTRY ALREADY?

YOU SHOULD LEAVE AS SOON AS YOU CAN.

DRESSROSA WILL BE IN GREAT CHAOS FOR THE NEXT DAY OR TWO.

SNORR——R

Y'KNOW, I STILL CAN'T GET OVER..

...THAT THERE WAS A THIRD BROTHER IN ADDITION TO ACE...

SNOR———R

LUFFY WAS THE MOST SURPRISED OF ANYONE, I'M SURE.

THAT FIGURES...

YEAH, IT'S THE FIRST I'VE HEARD OF IT.

CLINK

CLINK

GZ———z

!!

...I WAS PRONOUNCED DEAD YEARS AGO.

SS———H

AFTER ALL...

KZZ———z

HMM?

SHWUR———R

THAT'S WHAT WE SWORE WHEN WE SHARED THE CUPS OF BROTHERHOOD.

CLIII

NK!!

AND WE DECIDED WE'D GROW UP TO BE PIRATES...

OL' GARP WOULD TRY TO BEAT SOME SENSE INTO US...

ACE, LUFFY AND I RAISED ALL KINDS OF HELL WHEN WE WERE KIDS.

...WAS THE STRONG DESIRE **NOT** TO GO BACK TO MY PARENTS.

THE ONLY THING CLEAR TO ME...

I COULDN'T REMEMBER ANYTHING ELSE...

YOU WERE SUFFERING FROM MEMORY LOSS THAT WHOLE TIME?!

?!

IT WAS ONLY BECAUSE OF ACE...

IN A WAY, HE SAID, "YOU'RE SABO, BROTHER TO ME AND LUFFY!"

THAT'S WHAT I NOW BELIEVE.

SNOR——RR

CLINK CLINK

I'M SURPRISED YOUR MEMORY CAME BACK TO YOU.

BUT IS IVA ALL RIGHT?!

IT SAYS WHITEBEARD LOST!!

THERE'S AN ARTICLE ABOUT THE PARAMOUNT WAR!!!

IT DOESN'T MENTION IVA'S DEATH.

WHAM!!

THE FATALITIES ARE...

IT HAPPENED IN THE WORST POSSIBLE WAY...

...BUT PERHAPS THAT'S THE ONLY REASON HE WAS ABLE TO WAKE MY MEMORY...

YEAH!!! GOOD IDEA!!!

....!!!

!

WOULD YOU LET ME EAT...

...THE FLAME-FLAME FRUIT?

I GOT A GOOD LOOK AT HIM!

ALREADY?

WELL... SO LONG!

SNORR——R

IT'S THE ONLY ANSWER!!!

CREAK...

TAKE GOOD CARE OF HIM!!

WELL, I'M SURE LUFFY WILL CONTINUE TO BE A HAND-FUL, BUT...

I HAD IT MADE.

HERE, THIS IS LUFFY'S VIVRE CARD.

YEAH, PAL! YOU BET!!

RIP!

HERE, I'LL TAKE A LITTLE PIECE.

HUH? WHEN DID YOU DO THIS...?

CLINK!

BZAP!

BZAP!

FLAP

YEAH, I JUST SAW HIM.

SABO? THIS IS HACK.

CAW CAW

CLICK!

RR!! RR R

I'LL BE BACK SOON!!

THUMP!

0000!!

PFFT!

HE SOUNDS JUST LIKE ACE DID...

WATCH OUT, HACK! BE CAREFUL!!

WHY DID HE HANG UP?! THAT WAS IMPORTANT!!

WHOOSH

SEE AH!!

000

3 4

NUR-MUR *MUR-MUR*

BOOP!! BOOP...!

CLICK!!

UNDERSTOOD. AND HOW IS LUFFY? HE SEEMED VERY--

LET'S HURRY!

FLAP FLAP

YEP, WHENEVER I WANT.

DO

AND YOU CAN PRODUCE IT AT ANY MOMENT?

OM!!!

(A-P, Tochigi)

Q: Oda Sensei… N-nice to…ugh! *Flop!* As a matter of fact…I've fallen ill with a terrible case of Loving-Cora-Itis. So can you tell me Cora's height and his favorite and least favorite foods? I'm so obsessed, I can't find a boyfriend.

--Maiden in Love

A: That sounds awful. I'll write you a prescription. Take the following medications: "Nine-foot-seven," "Likes: lettuce, cabbage, pickled plums," "Dislikes: bread, pizza." Please take care.

Q: Hiya, Odacchi!! Wait, so the kid wearing the "bear" shirt in Chapter 785 of Volume 78 was **wearing that bear?!!**

--Bartholomew Kuma, Age 12

A: Yes. Well, I suppose I should explain this. (laughs) In Chapter 785 of the previous volume, there's a mother looking for her child amid the chaos. He's wearing a "bear shirt," she says. At the end of the chapter, Fujitora helps mother and son find each other, and if you look closely at his shirt…

HE'S ONLY FIVE, AND HE'S WEARING A BEAR SHIRT! PLEASE!!

PLEASE, HAS ANYONE SEEN MY SON?!!

Not this Kuma (Bear)

But this Kuma

You will see that it was all a bit of a joke since "kuma" means "Bear" in Japanese. So let's all end the SBS by letting this mother and son hear it. Ready, set…

You mean that "Bear"?!!

See you again next volume!! There's some more stuff at the end, so check it out.

Chapter 795:
SUICIDE

REQUEST: "NAMI GIVING AN UGLY GORILLA A MAKEOVER"
BY SAYAMAKKO T.K. FROM SAITAMA

DRESS-ROSA

SO... WHAT'S THE ROLL?

BE MY EYES FOR ME.

!!

UP!

UH... IT'S A **ONE**!!

CL

THEN THEY'VE WON THIS ROUND... NO ARRESTS TONIGHT.

YES, WE DID, BUT--!!

FSSHHH-!

...WAS STRAW'S NUMBER, NO?

AND WE AGREED THAT ONE...

MURMUR

MURMUR

BUT, ISSHO! WE RAN ALL OVER THE ENTIRE COUNTRY TO TRACK DOWN THEIR LOCATION!!

...AND THEN QUIBBLE WITH THE RESULT AFTER THE ROLL. IT'S UNBECOMIN'...

A MAN DOESN'T THROW THE DICE...

THIS IS OUR BEST CHANCE TO BRING IN LAW AND STRAW HAT!!

AND AFTER THAT BIG BLOWUP WITH THE FLEET ADMIRAL!!

OH, COME ON!!

MAYNARD!!

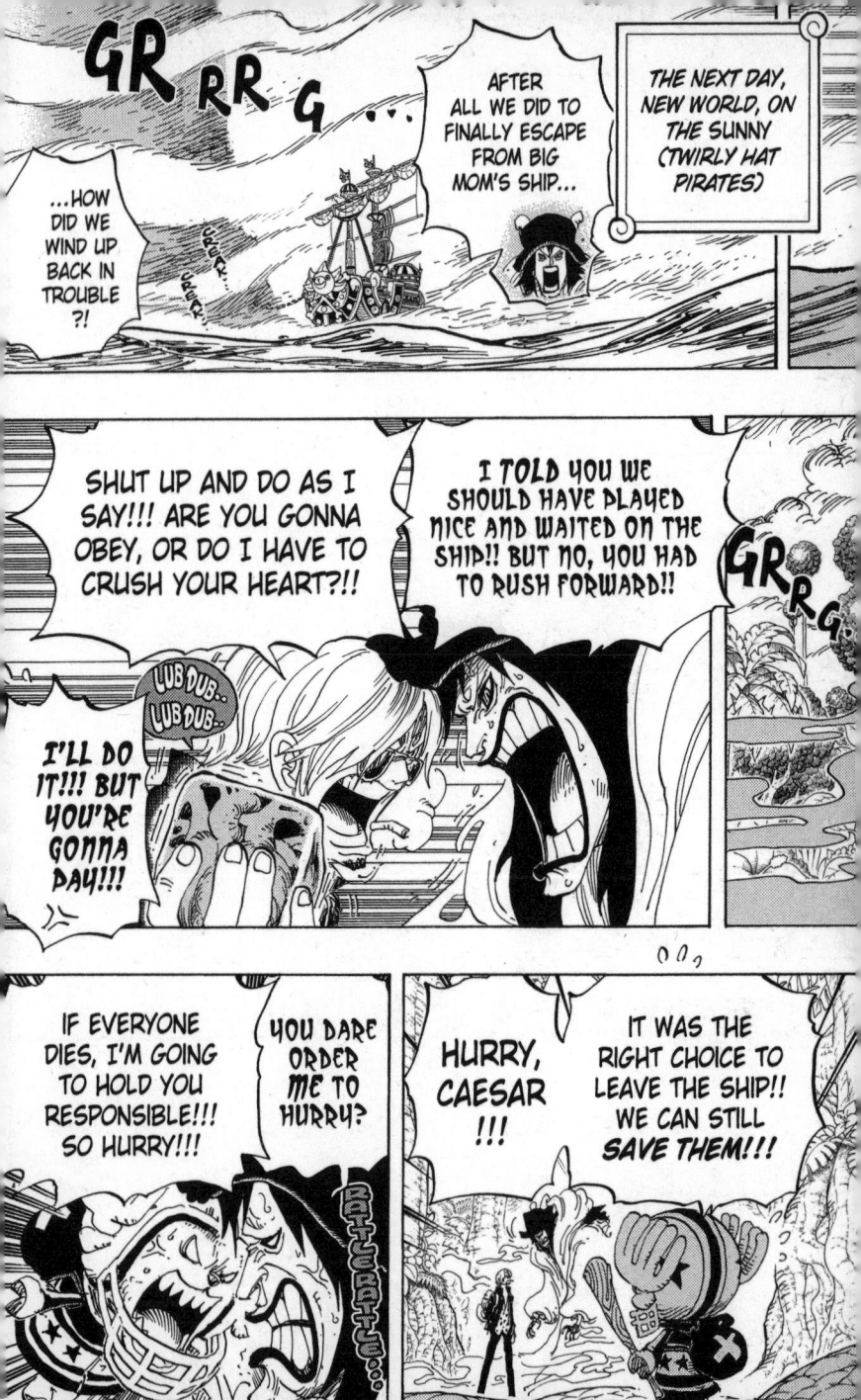

BOOOM!!

AAARGH !!! **ZABLOOSH!!** EEEEK !!!

I WILL PROTECT US FROM WHATEVER COMES!!

ZZSH...

RAIN?! THAT'S MORE LIKE A SOLID FLOOD!!

WHUP!!

YOU POWER USERS ARE MORE TROUBLE THAN YOU'RE WORTH!!!

ARGH!!

AAAH AAAH AAAH

BLUB BLUB

HELP MEEEE !!!

ME TOO !!

SPLASH SPLASH...!!

NAMI !!!

MOMONO-SUKE!!

REPORT THAT *THERE WAS NO SAMURAI!!*

WE'VE PUSHED THEM THIS FAR, AND STILL NO SIGN OF HIM!

WHAT?!! BUT WE STILL HAVEN'T FOUND THE SAMURAI!

RETREAT!! MASTER SHEEPSHEAD IS DOWN!!

ZWAP!!

RIGHT AWAY!!

...

WELL, AS LONG AS SHE'S SAFE...

PERHAPS SHE GOT AWAY...

SO... WHERE'D THAT GIRL GO?

THE WATER'S DRAINING...

WHAT WAS THAT ALL ABOUT?

ZZSHHH...

GRRGG

WE MUST HURRY.

THERE'S NOT A MOMENT TO WASTE!!

GRRG

IT'S CHOPPEREMON! HE'S IN THE LOWER FOREST!

HEY, EVERY-ONE!! COME QUICK!!!

...THAT HE WAS SEARCHING FOR A PLACE TO DIE.

THE MAN CLAIMED...

...HE HAD TASTED DEFEAT AS A PIRATE ON SEVEN OCCASIONS...

IF HE'S SERIOUS, I WON'T STOP HIM...

TO SPEAK MORE ON THIS MAN...

...AND BEEN CAUGHT BY THE NAVY OR ENEMY SHIPS NO LESS THAN 18 TIMES!!

AND FINALLY, HE ATTEMPTED SUICIDE.

HE WAS TORTURED TIME AND TIME AGAIN, AND LIVED AS A PRISONER.

THE VERY RARE ACT OF SUICIDE BY JUMPING FROM A SKY ISLAND...

HUP...!!

AMEN.

TO BE CONTINUED IN *ONE PIECE*, VOL. 80!

I GUESS...THERE'S NO CHOICE BUT TO GO THROUGH WITH IT!!!

OLD WHITE-BEARD DID IT RIGHT...

DAMN IT ALL... HURRY UP, JOKER!! PREPARE FOR THE FINAL BATTLE!!!

LET THIS DREARY WORLD BE DESTROYED!!! LET'S START THE GREATEST WAR THIS PLANET HAS EVER SEEN!!!

...THIS PIRATE IS SAID TO BE THE STRONGEST CREATURE ALIVE!!!

CHARACTER LIST!!

A special list so you can see who was born on what day easily!!

Jan~Apr

January

	1	2	3	4	5	6
January	Portgaz D. Ace / Daz Bones (Mr. 1) / Isle One	Peepley Lulu	Iceberg / Aisa	Crocus / Peterman	Strawberry	Oimo / Tilestone
	7	**8**	**9**	**10**	**11**	**12**	**13**
	Mozu	Emporio Ivankov	Pickles	Eustass Kid / Otohime	Itomimizu	Hiriluk	Ikaros Much
	14	**15**	**16**	**17**	**18**	**19**	**20**
	Sweetpea	A.O.		Capone Bege	Splash & Splatta	Spandine	
	21	**22**	**23**	**24**	**25**	**26**	**27**
						Nero	Lola
	28	**29**	**30**	**31**			
				Aladdin			

February

	1	2	3	4	5	6
February	Broggy / Doma	Killer / Nefeltari Vivi	Brownbeard / Bizarre / Fuza	Gloriosa / Haruta / Fukaboshi	Vista / Blamenco	Nico Robin / Nico Olvia / Blondie
	7	**8**	**9**	**10**	**11**	**12**	**13**
		Onigumo / Gonbe	Bartholomew Kuma / Wadatsumi / Genbo	Mikazuki		Little Oars Jr.	
	14	**15**	**16**	**17**	**18**	**19**	**20**
		Charlotte Linlin / Daisy	Bluejam				Kumadori
	21	**22**	**23**	**24**	**25**	**26**	**27**
		Jerry / Hamburg	Makino	Genista			
	28	**29**					
	Woop Slap						

Check birthdays at a glance!

ONE PIECE BIRTHDAY REFERENCE

March	1	2	3	4	5	6
	Minorhinoceros	Sanji / San Juan Wolf	Galdino (Mr. 3) / Hina	Masira / Minotaur	Sadie / Minokoala	Jaguar D. Saul / Salome
	7 Minozebra	**8** Zambai	**9** Franky / Shanks / Dracule Mihawk	**10** Sentomaru / Satori / Nola	**11** Spandam / Palms	**12** Stelly	**13** Lafitte
	14 Alvida / Smoker	**15**	**16** Tom	**17**	**18**	**19** Scratchmen Apoo / Atomos	**20** Sabo / Shiki
	21 Lieutenant Spacey	**22**	**23**	**24** Thatch	**25** Ohm	**26** Tsuru	**27**
	28	**29** Catarina Devon / Shalria	**30** Mamboshi	**31** Baskerville			

April	1	2	3	4	5	6
	Usopp / Kashii	Zeff / Jimbei	Brook / Porchemy / Monda	Shirahoshi / Foxy	Yamakaji / Right Minister	Edward Newgate / Speed Jil / Jean Bart
	7	**8** Clover / Megalo	**9** Caesar Clown / Marguerite / Mohmoo / Yorki	**10** Forest Boss	**11**	**12**	**13** Morgan
	14 Hody Jones	**15** Fossa	**16** Stronger	**17**	**18** Hyouzou	**19**	**20** Blueno
	21	**22** Kuro	**23** Kalifa	**24**	**25**	**26**	**27**
	28 Funkfreed	**29** Ms. Golden Week	**30**				

LIST PART 2!!

WHO CARES ABOUT BIRTH-DAYS?

May~ Aug

May

May	1 Kaido / Capote	2 Monkey D. Garp / Coribou	3 Arlong	4 Ishily	5 Monkey D. Luffy / Demaro Black (Fake Luffy)	6 Eneru
7	8 Shakuyaku	9 Sengoku / Kong	10 Heracles	11	12	13 Silvers Rayleigh / Koby
14	15	16	17	18 Gorilla	19 Andre / John Giant	20 Conis
21	22 Decalvan Bros.	23 Choo	24	25 Big Bun	26	27
28	29	30	31 Lacuba			

June

June	1 Charlos / Moda	2 Rob Lucci / Chimney / Lonz	3 Musse	4 Epoida	5 Jabra	6 Karma / Momonga
7 Perona	8 Saldeath / Lacroix	9 Surume / Rockstar	10 Dalton / Portgaz D. Rouge	11 Shiryu	12 Disco	13
14	15	16	17	18	19	20 Amadobu
21	22 Gyro	23	24 Ryuboshi	25	26	27
28 Roswald	29 Fukuro	30 Elmy				

ONE PIECE CHARACTER BIRTHDAY REFERENCE

July

	1	2	3	4	5	6
		Left Minister	Nami Neptune	Caribou		Lucky Roux Namule
7 Raki	**8** Daruma Paulie	**9**	**10** Kamakiri Ranba	**11**	**12**	**13**
14	**15** Corazon (Rocinante)	**16** Helmeppo Seto	**17** Hammond	**18**	**19**	**20**
21	**22**	**23** Richie	**24**	**25**	**26**	**27**
28	**29** Kadar	**30**	**31**			

August

	1	2	3	4	5	6
	Urouge Aphelandra	Yasopp	Marshall D. Teech Inazuma	Earth Boss Amazon	Vasco Shot Gaimon Octopako	Sodomu & Gomora Blenheim
7 Bellamy Kaku	**8** Buggy Hatchan	**9** Wapol Hack Vegapunk	**10** Issho (Fujitora) Gedatsu Hattori	**11** Duval	**12**	**13**
14	**15** Bentham (Bon Clay) Dr. Tsukimi	**16** Sakazuki	**17**	**18** Wyper	**19** Motobaro	**20**
21	**22** Vander Decken IX	**23**	**24**	**25** Corgi	**26**	**27** Monet
28 Hannyabal	**29**	**30** Curly Dadan	**31** Cavendish			

LIST PART 3!!

WHO DO YOU SHARE A BIRTHDAY WITH?

Sep~ Dec

September

	1	2	3	4	5	6
	Jewelry Bonney / Kiwi / Delacuahi	Boa Hancock	Boa Sandersonia / Brannew / Mcguy	Kumacy / Wanze	Crocodile / Boa Marigold	Gecko Moria / Squard / Macro
	7	8	9	10	11	12	13
		Cabaji / Rakuyo	Basil Hawkins / Sharley	T. Bone / Berrygood	Montblanc Cricket	Curiel	Hoe
	14	15	16	17	18	19	20
		Spoil	Laboon / Rindo		Devil Diaz	Krieg	Shura
	21	22	23	24	25	26	27
	Kuzan / Pappagu			Su			
	28	29	30				
			Avalo Pisaro				

October

	1	2	3	4	5	6
	Komille / Mohji	Dorry / Tonjit	Yama	Oars / Kalgara	Monkey D. Dragon / Marco / Van Ogre / Kokoro	Trafalgar Law / Tashigi / Bartolomeo
	7	8	9	10	11	12	13
		Doberman / Pierre	Magellan / Montblanc Noland / Dosun	Den			Izo
	14	15	16	17	18	19	20
	Haredas		Taroimo		Doc. Q		Tyrannosaurus
	21	22	23	24	25	26	27
			Don Quixote Doflamingo	X. Drake	Koala / Kuroobi		
	28	29	30	31			
			Domino / Magura	Sherry / Whitey Bay			

ONE PIECE CHARACTER BIRTHDAY REFERENCE

November

	1	2	3	4	5	6
November	Dalmation		Camie	Kashigami	Fisher Tiger	Ryuma
7 Holly	8	9 Benn Beckman Albion Jalmack	10	11 Roronoa Zolo Jozu Zeo	12	13 Kingdew
14	15	16 Porche	17	18	19	20 Bepo
21	22	23 Borsalino Ankoro	24 Ran	25	26 Goro	27
28	29	30				

December

	1	2	3	4	5	6
December					5 Indigo	
7	8	9	10	11	12	13
14	15	16	17	18	19 Hogback Dogura	20
21	22 Ganfor	23	24 Tony Tony Chopper	25 Jesus Burgess	26	27
28	29	30 Absalom	31 Gol D. Roger			

Look up your favorite character's birthday!!

COMING NEXT VOLUME:

With Doflamingo finally defeated, peace has returned to Dressrosa! The Straw Hats have saved the people of the island, but they're still wanted pirates. With the Navy on its way, Luffy and company will need to slip out while it's still safe. But first, there's some unfinished business...

ON SALE NOVEMBER 2016!

You're Reading in the Wrong Direction!!

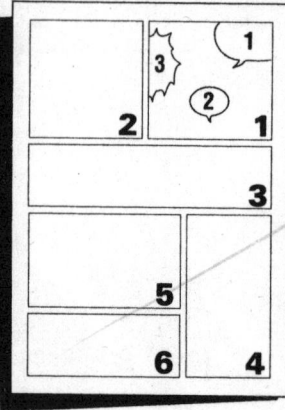

Whoops! Guess what? You're starting at the wrong end of the comic!

...It's true! In keeping with the original Japanese format, **One Piece** is meant to be read from right to left, starting in the upper-right corner.

Unlike English, which is read from left to right, Japanese is read from right to left, meaning that action, sound effects and word-balloon order are completely reversed...something which can make readers unfamiliar with Japanese feel pretty backwards themselves. For this reason, manga or Japanese comics published in the U.S. in English have sometimes been published "flopped"—that is, printed in exact reverse order, as though seen from the other side of a mirror.

By flopping pages, U.S. publishers can avoid confusing readers, but the compromise is not without its downside. For one thing, a character in a flopped manga series who once wore in the original Japanese version a T-shirt emblazoned with "M A Y" (as in "the merry month of") now wears one which reads "Y A M"! Additionally, many manga creators in Japan are themselves unhappy with the process, as some feel the mirror-imaging of their art skews their original intentions.

We are proud to bring you Eiichiro Oda's **One Piece** in the original unflopped format. For now, though, turn to the other side of the book and let the journey begin...!

—Editor